Tweet

ISBN 978 1 938068 34 8

Library of Congress Control Number: 2018966628

Published by Oxvision Books
4001 Tamiami Trail North, Suite 250, Naples, FL 34103

Find us at: **oxvisionmedia.com** & **tweetlove.com**

PUBLISHED BY

OXVISION
BOOKS

ARTIST
Tim Ladwig

AUTHOR
Brian Oxley

To Dallas & Sharon Frazier, our friends

When someone says something
to you that's unkind, and the
wish to hurt back is what fills
your mind, say something nice,
leave meanness behind, and
tweet love.

When something shows up
on your screen that's not right,
someone wrote something that
could start a fight, close down
that screen, get it out of your
sight, and tweet love.

When people you thought were
your friends turn their backs...

And you feel like staging a counterattack, make a new friend, or two, or even a pack—and tweet love.

When someone around
you is angry or mad...

Figure out what's making their
day seem so bad. You might find
a way to help them feel glad,
and tweet love.

When you're feeling deserted,
or scared, or alone, or you feel
like you're lost and can't find
your home...

Remember the place where your name is known, and tweet love.

When you have a sickness that won't go away, just close your eyes and imagine the day that God's promised to send all our sorrows away, and tweet love.

And when you see someone
who lives on the street,
don't look away—give them
something to eat...

But make sure you give
with a smile that is sweet,
and tweet love.

When people around you go low, you go high. When everyone around you crawls, you must try to rise up and soar like a bird in the sky, and tweet love.

When you're at the table and someone is cross, and this person is yelling and wants to be boss, sing a song as you pass them the crab apple sauce, and tweet love.

When you don't have the money
to go hear a band, and it's your
most favorite group and it would
have been grand, put on your
own concert with whatever's
at hand, and tweet love.

When your heart is broken and you want to cry, or you just feel empty and aren't even sure why, watch for blessings to fall like rain from the sky, and tweet love.

And when you're feeling ugly or broken or scared, remember God made you—you're His superstar. Remember He loves you just as you are, and tweet love.

Follow
GRANDPA
on his many adventures...

Find these books and others at oxvisionmedia.com or your favorite online retailer.

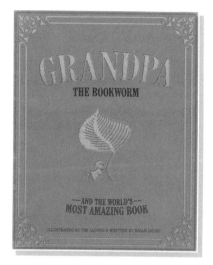

GRANDPA THE BOOKWORM AND THE WORLD'S MOST AMAZING BOOK

GRANDPA, HOW BIG IS YOUR LOVE?

GRANDPA'S DIET

GRANDPA'S TIMEOUT

GRANDPA SAVES THE DAY

GRANDPA'S OVERALLS

More Oxvision Books
for Young Readers

GRANDPA, THE MUSIC EXECUTIVE

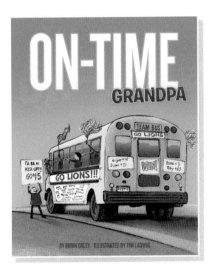

ON-TIME GRANDPA

LILY: THE GIRL WHO COULD SEE

**W.S. "FLUKE" HOLLAND:
THE FATHER OF THE DRUMS**

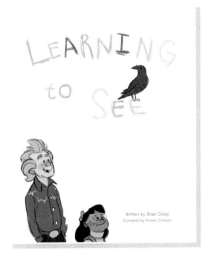

LEARNING TO SEE

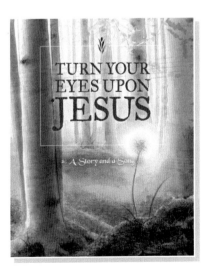

**TURN YOUR EYES UPON JESUS
A STORY AND A SONG**

OXVISION
BOOKS

Made in the
USA
Middletown, DE